Supporting
Writing
Skills

FOR AGES 5–6

Andrew
Brodie

Introduction

Supporting Writing Skills is aimed at all those who work with children who have been identified as needing 'additional' or 'different' literacy support. It can be used by anyone working with children who fall into this category, whether you are a teacher, classroom assistant or parent.

Typically the five to six year-old children for whom the book is intended will be working at the levels expected of Pre-school or Reception children or may simply need extra help in tackling the level of work appropriate for Year 1. Their difficulties may be short term, and overcome with extra practice and support on a one-to-one or small group basis, or they may be long term, where such support enables them to make progress but at a level behind their peer group.

The activities in this book provide exactly what these children need – plenty of writing activities linked to the work that they will be completing in other areas of the curriculum. All the activities provide excellent opportunities for speaking and listening and most pages include reading practice in addition to the main writing task. Each activity page includes brief 'Notes for teachers' so that the pages can be picked up and used quickly and effectively.

The 2006 Framework for teaching Literacy lists twelve strands for literacy development. Strands 1 to 4 concern Speaking and Listening; Strands 5 to 12 concern Reading and Writing. The writing activities in this book have been created to match many of the key elements of the Framework's reading and writing strands for Foundation Stage and Year 1:

5. Apply phonic knowledge and skills as the prime approach to reading and spelling unfamiliar words that are not completely decodable; read and spell phonically decodable two-syllable and three-syllable words

6. Spell new words using phonics as the prime approach; segment sounds into their constituent phonemes in order to spell them correctly

7. Extend their vocabulary, exploring the meanings and sounds of new words; show an understanding of the elements of stories, such as main character, sequence of events

8. Visualise and comment on events, characters and ideas

9. Use key features of narrative in their own writing; convey information and ideas in simple non-narrative forms; find and use new and interesting words and phrases, including story language; create short simple texts on paper that combine words with images

10. Write chronological and non-chronological texts using simple structures

11. Compose and write simple sentences independently to communicate meaning; use capital letters and full stops when punctuating simple sentences

12. Write most letters, correctly formed and orientated, using a comfortable and efficient pencil grip; write with spaces between words accurately.

This book consists of three main sections:

Section 1 (pages 5–33)

Worksheets 1 to 29 contain activities to encourage the process of spelling new words, through use of phonic skills, as well as providing many opportunities for creating simple sentences. Sentences with clear punctuation are modelled for the pupils, then the activities promote the construction of accurate sentences that start with capital letters and end with full stops. Some pages require pupils to write just one sentence, using relevant vocabulary, while others require several sentences on a particular theme. Emphasis is also placed on practising the correct formation of letters and numerals.

Section 2 (pages 35–49)

With two sets of narrative sheets, pupils are encouraged to work out the correct sequence of a set of sentences and to combine these with the images provided. From this speaking, listening and reading activity the children move on to rewriting the text within a simple 'book' presentation.

Section 3 (pages 51–63)

An important resource contained within this book is the word bank that can be created from the final fourteen sheets. This contains all the high frequency words recommended for Reception, together with all the additional words used in this book. These words can be used for reading practice as well as for the creation of simple sentences using the writing lines on the final sheet of the book.

Contents

Record and Review

Name: _____ Date of birth: _____

Teacher: _____ Class: _____

Support assistant: _____

Code of Practice stage: _____ Date targets set: _____

Target

1 _____

2 _____

3 _____

4 _____

Review

Target

1 _____

_____

_____ Target achieved? ☐ Date: _____

2 _____

_____

_____ Target achieved? ☐ Date: _____

3 _____

_____

_____ Target achieved? ☐ Date: _____

4 _____

_____

_____ Target achieved? ☐ Date: _____

Name: Tommy Wheeler   **Date:** 19·7·17

This is a monster.

He is called Jim.

This   is   Jim.

This is Jim This is J im

Notes for teachers

Children need lots of opportunities for speaking and listening before they can become effective writers. Discuss the picture with the child and read the text, saying the words very clearly so that s/he can hear the phonemes within each word. When s/he is ready, demonstrate writing the sentence 'This is Jim' using handwriting according to the school's handwriting policy. Make sure the child watches you write the sentence then ask her/him to copy it underneath. Point out the capital letters for the start of the sentence and for the start of the name Jim, and the full stop at the end of the sentence.

Name: **Date:**

Draw a monster.

What is your monster called?

This is ___Tommy Kaci___

Notes for teachers

Discuss ideas with the child that will help her/him to draw their own monster. This is the first step towards imaginative story creation. Help the child to choose a name for the monster then write this name for her/him in the space provided. When s/he is ready, demonstrate writing the sentence 'This is ... ' using handwriting according to the school's handwriting policy. Make sure the child watches you write the sentence and then ask her/him to copy it underneath. Point out the capital letters for the start of the sentence and for the start of the name, and the full stop at the end of the sentence.

Here is Jim the monster.

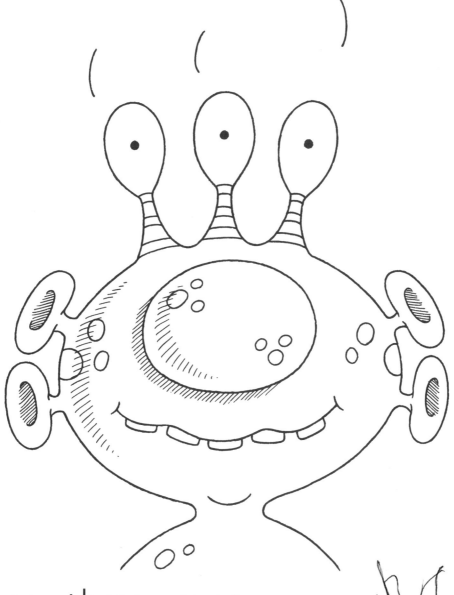

Jim has three eyes.

Jim has three eyes. JIM

Notes for teachers
Children need lots of opportunities for speaking and listening before they can become effective writers. Discuss the picture with the child and read the writing, saying the words very clearly so that s/he can hear the phonemes within each word. When s/he is ready, demonstrate writing the sentence 'Jim has three eyes' using handwriting according to the school's handwriting policy. Make sure the child watches you write the sentence and then ask her/him to copy it underneath. Point out the capital letter for the start of the name Jim, and the full stop at the end of the sentence.

Andrew Brodie: Supporting Writing Skills © A & C Black Publishers Ltd. 2007

Name: _____   **Date:** _____

Here is Jim the monster.

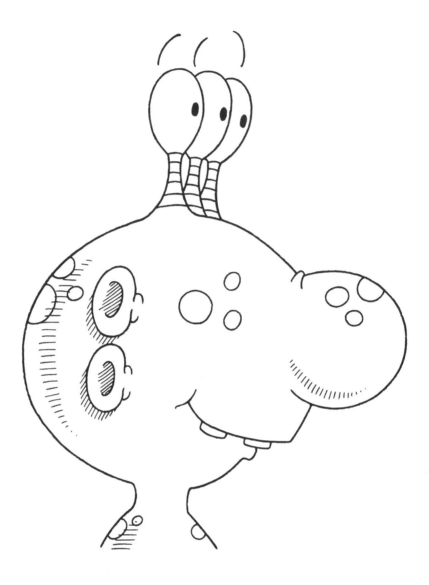

Jim has a big nose.

_____

_____

Notes for teachers

Discuss the picture with the child and read the text, saying the words very clearly so that s/he can hear the phonemes within each word. When s/he is ready, demonstrate writing the sentence 'Jim has a big nose' using handwriting according to the school's handwriting policy. Make sure that the child watches you write the sentence and then ask her/him to copy it underneath. Point out the capital letter for the start of the name Jim, and the full stop at the end of the sentence.

Andrew Brodie: Supporting Writing Skills © A & C Black Publishers Ltd. 2007

Jim is waving.

Jim's hand has four fingers.

_____

_____

Notes for teachers

Discuss the picture with the child and read the text, saying the words very clearly so that s/he can hear the phonemes within each word. When s/he is ready, demonstrate writing the sentence 'Jim's hand has four fingers' using handwriting according to the school's handwriting policy. Make sure that the child watches you write the sentence and then ask her/him to copy it underneath. Point out the capital letter for the start of the name Jim, and the full stop at the end of the sentence.

Jim is showing us his foot.

Jim's foot has two toes.

_____

_____

Notes for teachers
Discuss the picture with the child and read the text, saying the words very clearly so that s/he can hear the phonemes within each word. When s/he is ready, demonstrate writing the sentence 'Jim's foot has two toes' using handwriting according to the school's handwriting policy. Make sure that the child watches you write the sentence and then ask her/him to copy it underneath. Point out the capital letter for the start of the name Jim, and the full stop at the end of the sentence.

one   nose

   two   hands

three   eyes

Jim   has   one   nose.   He   has
two   hands   and   three   eyes.

Notes for teachers
Discuss the pictures with the child. Read the text and help her/him to copy the number phrases. Encourage her/him to copy the two sentences using capital letters at the start and full stops at the end.

Name: Date:

WORD BANK

head   arm   body   hand

fingers   leg   foot   toes

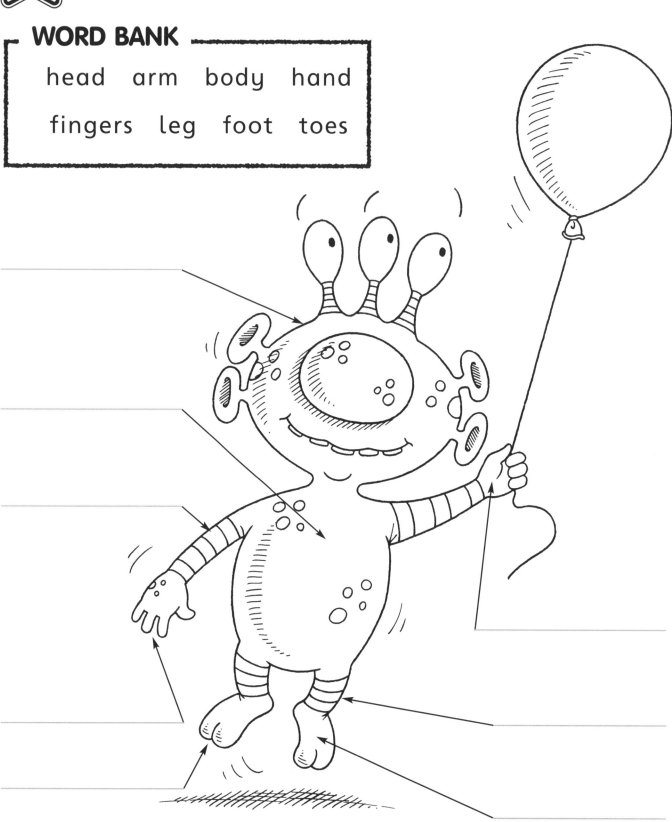

Write the words in the correct places.

Notes for teachers

Discuss the picture with the child. Read the words in the word bank and help her/him to write these words in the correct places. This work links well with the science topic 'Ourselves' where children may be asked to label a picture of a child.

WORD BANK

ear   eye   nose

mouth   tooth   chin

Write the words in the correct places.

Notes for teachers
Discuss the picture with the child. Read the words in the word bank and help her/him to write these words in the correct places. This work links well with the science topic 'Ourselves' where children may be asked to label a picture of a child.

Andrew Brodie: Supporting Writing Skills © A & C Black Publishers Ltd. 2007

13

Name: **Date:**

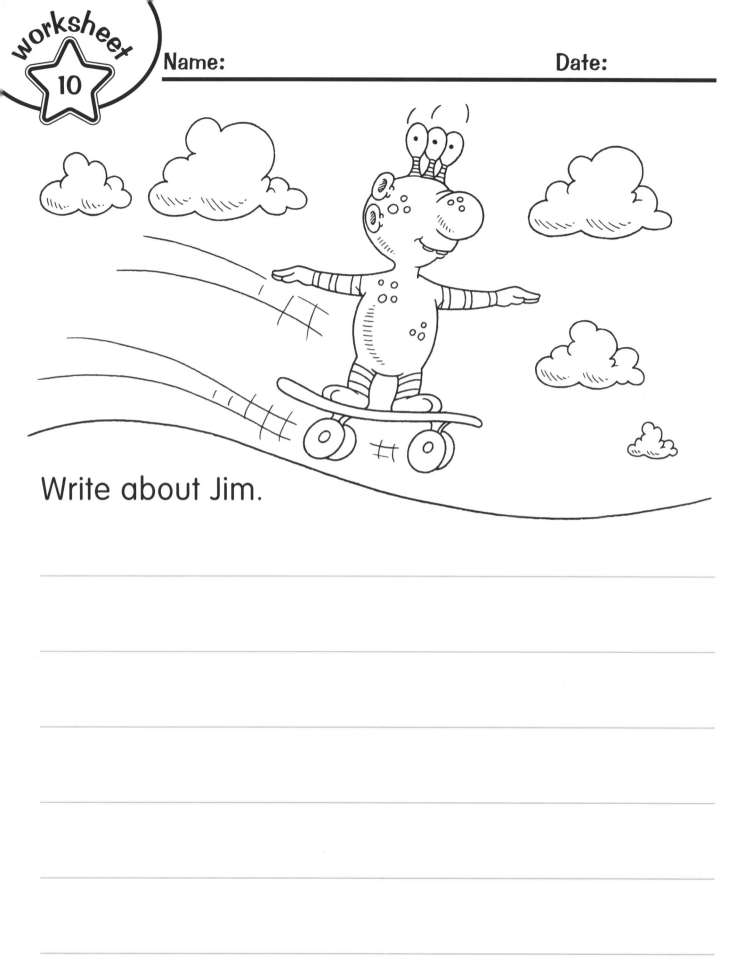

Write about Jim.

Notes for teachers
By now the child has learnt a lot about Jim the monster. Use this sheet to encourage her/him to make up and write down
a sentence about Jim. Help the child to segment each word that s/he wants to use into its phonemes so that s/he can 'hear'
how to spell it. You may like the child to construct the sentence using the words and writing lines from the Resource
sheets at the back of this book before s/he attempts to write it.

Name: _____ **Date:** _____

Jim can write the alphabet. Can you?

a   b   c   d   e   f   g

h   i   j   k   l   m   n

o   p   q   r   s   t   u

v   w   x   y   z

Notes for teachers

Help the child read the letters of the alphabet, saying the names of the letters and the sounds that they usually make e.g. this is the letter b and it says /b/. Help the child to copy the letters carefully, paying particular attention to ascenders and descenders. Make sure, for example, that the child writes the letter j so that it passes through the line like a letter g.

Name: **Date:**

Jim can write the alphabet
in capital letters. Can you?

A   B   C   D   E   F   G

H   I   J   K   L   M   N

O   P   Q   R   S   T   U

V   W   X   Y   Z

Notes for teachers

Help the child to read the letters of the alphabet. Discuss the fact that the letters are capital letters and that we use capital letters at the starts of sentences or for names. Say the names of the letters and the sounds that they usually make e.g. this is letter D and it says /d/. Help the child to copy the letters carefully, starting and finishing at the correct point.

Name: _____   **Date:** _____

Jim can write numbers.

0 1 2 3 4 5 6 7 8 9

     How many stamps?

    How many stamps?

How many stamps?

Notes for teachers
Help the child to read the numbers, including the zero, then help her/him to copy them carefully starting and finishing at the correct point.

On Monday Jim writes a story.

On Tuesday Jim plays football.

On Wednesday Jim paints a picture.

On Thursday Jim skips.

On Friday Jim reads a book.

Notes for teachers

Use this sheet as an introduction to the days of the week activity on Worksheet 15. Help the child read the sentences.
Point out the capital letters at the start of each sentence, for the days of the week and for Jim's name.

Andrew Brodie: Supporting Writing Skills © A & C Black Publishers Ltd. 2007

Name: **Date:**

Monday

_____

Tuesday

_____

Wednesday

_____

Thursday

_____

Friday

_____

Notes for teachers

Use Worksheet 14 as an introduction to this worksheet. Help the child to read the days of the week. Read each word slowly and carefully to help the child segment the word into its phonemes for spelling. Point out the capital letter at the start of each word and then ask the child to copy the words carefully on the writing lines underneath.

Andrew Brodie: Supporting Writing Skills © A & C Black Publishers Ltd. 2007

It is the weekend.

Jim swims
on Saturday.

On Sunday Jim eats
too much.

He goes to sleep.

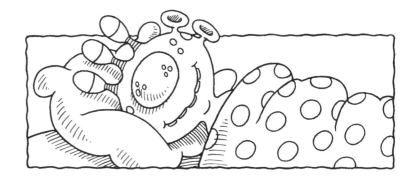

Notes for teachers
Use this sheet as an introduction to the activity on Worksheet 17. Help the child to read the sentences. Point out the capital letter at the start of each sentence, for the days of the week and for Jim's name.

Saturday

_____

Sunday

_____

Jim is asleep.

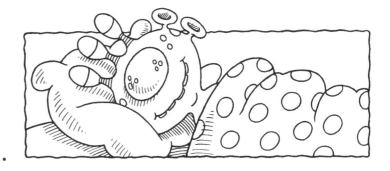

_____ .

Notes for teachers
Use Worksheet 16 as an introduction to this worksheet. Help the child to read the weekend days, Saturday and Sunday.
Read each word slowly and carefully to help the child segment the word into its phonemes for spelling. Point out the
capital letters at the start of each word and then ask the child to copy the words and the short sentence on to the writing
lines underneath.

Name: **Date:**

What do you do on Monday?

_____

_____

_____

Notes for teachers

This worksheet can be used as a follow up to the activities on Worksheets 14 to 17. You could help the child compose a sentence using the words and writing lines on the Resource sheets at the back of this book, before s/he attempts to write it.

What do you do on Saturday?

_____

_____

_____

_____

Notes for teachers
This worksheet can be used as a follow up to the activities on Worksheets 14 to 17. You could help the child to compose a sentence using the words and writing lines from the Resource sheets at the back of this book, before s/he attempts to write it.

Name: _____   **Date:** _____

This is Jim's shopping list.

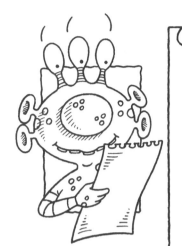

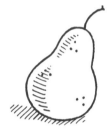

apple

_____

pear

_____

banana

_____

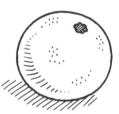

orange

_____

milk

_____

Notes for teachers

Discuss the list with the child. Say each word slowly, encouraging the child to hear the phonemes. S/he should say the word out loud as s/he writes it. Discuss the fact that this is Jim's shopping list. What type of food does he buy? What type of food does the child like? (Children in this age group will be studying food as part of their work in Design Technology).

Write your own shopping list.

Draw pictures to go with it.

Name: **Date:**

Here are Jim's friends.

Millie   Molly

Here are my friends.

My friends are

Millie and Molly.

Notes for teachers

Use this sheet as an introduction to the activity on Worksheet 23. Discuss the fact that there are two sentences. Help the child to read the sentences. Point out the capital letters at the start of each sentence and for the names of Jim's friends. You could take this opportunity to discuss the endings of the words Millie and Molly. Both names end with the phoneme /ee/ but the graphemes are different.

Name: **Date:**

Draw your friends.

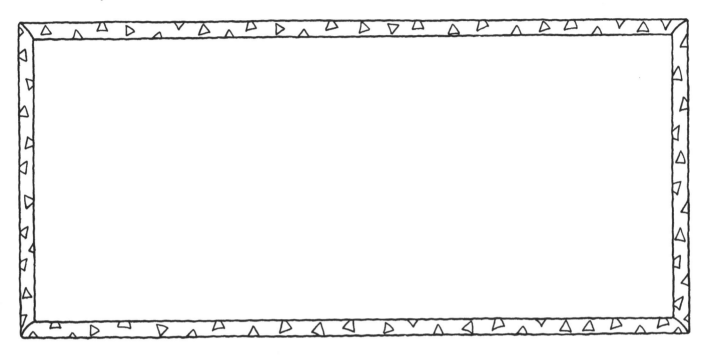

Write about your friends.

Notes for teachers

Use this sheet after discussing Worksheet 22 with the child. You could help the child compose each sentence using the words and writing lines from the Resource sheets at the back of this book, before s/he attempts to write it. Help her/him to segment the names that s/he wishes to use into their constituent phonemes before attempting to spell them. Correct these spellings if necessary.

Here is Jim's teacher.

She is called Mrs Dunn.

Here is my teacher.

My teacher is Mrs Dunn.

Notes for teachers
Use this sheet as an introduction to the activity on Worksheet 25. Discuss the fact that Jim has written two sentences.
Help the child to read the sentences. Point out the capital letter at the start of each sentence and for 'Mrs' and 'Dunn'.

Name: **Date:**

Draw your teacher.

Write about your teacher.

Notes for teachers
Use this sheet after discussing Worksheet 24 with the child. You could help the child compose each sentence by using the words and writing lines from the Resource sheets at the back of this book, before s/he attempts to write it. Help her/him to segment the name that s/he wishes to use into its constituent phonemes before attempting to spell it. Correct the spelling if necessary.

Name: _____   **Date:** _____

This is Jim's house.

WORD BANK

roof   door   window   wall

Jim's house   chimney

Write the words in the correct places.

Notes for teachers
Children in this age group will be studying houses and homes as part of their work in Design Technology. This worksheet provides an opportunity for an individual child to look closely at a picture of a house and at relevant words, before s/he meets the topic in class.

Name: _____ **Date:** _____

This is Jim's address.

7 Monster Lane,

Scaretown,

Frightshire,

SC3 2MN

Do you know your address?

Write your address.

Notes for teachers

Children in this age group will be studying houses and homes as part of their work in Design Technology and addresses as part of their work in Geography. Help the child to read the introductory sentence. Read Jim's address to her/him. As in most addresses, the words are difficult to read and we would not expect the child to be able to read them unaided. Point out the postcode, explaining that this is not a word but a mixture of capital letters and numbers. S/he will need help in writing her/his own address. If s/he does not know the address you could use the school address instead.

Name:

Date:

Jim is on holiday.

He is at the seaside.

Notes for teachers

Children in this age group will be studying seaside holidays in the past as part of their History work. This sheet introduces the seaside as a possible setting for the child's own story writing. Encourage the child to copy the sentences following the school's handwriting policy.

Can you remember your holiday?

Notes for teachers

Children in this age group will be studying seaside holidays in the past as part of their History work. Some sensitivity will be required in giving this sheet to a child who may not have been on holiday. In this case, discuss what the child can remember about a day out at a weekend or during the school holidays. Help the child to draw a picture and compose a sentence about the holiday. You may like to repeat the sentence several times back to the child, saying each word slowly and carefully, to help her/him to segment the words into their phonemes to make them easier to spell. You could ask the child to create the sentence using the words and writing lines from the Resource sheets at the back of this book.

Notes for teachers on Worksheets 30 to 36

The next seven worksheets feature a simple story about Jim the monster. The activities will help the child to begin to create a piece of writing in a narrative form, possibly over several lessons. They also include vocabulary related to 'push and pull' in the Science topic of movement.

Worksheets 30–34

The first four sheets each feature a picture of Jim and a baby monster. These pictures should be photocopied then introduced to the child one at a time and not necessarily in the correct order. In each case ask the child what the picture shows. The opportunity to discuss the picture is an excellent speaking and listening activity. Praise the child for finding all the details in the picture.

Having discussed the pictures, photocopy and cut out the four sentences on Worksheet 34. Read these with the child and then help her/him to match the sentences to the pictures to make a story. This sequencing activity provides opportunities for lots of speaking and listening as well as considerable reading practice.

The correct order of the sentences is as follows:

This is Jim and a baby monster.
Jim pushes the pushchair.
Jim gets very tired.
The baby monster pulls Jim home.

Worksheets 35–36

Photocopy Worksheets 35 and 36 back to back on to a single sheet. This can then be folded to make a simple four-page book. Help the child write a sentence to go with the pictures on each page of their book. The child could simply copy the sentences provided or you could help her/him to compose her/his own sentences. If this is the case, encourage her/him to segment the words into their phonemes in order to spell them.

Name: _____   **Date:** _____

Name: _____

Date: _____

Name: _____ **Date:** _____

Name: _____ **Date:** _____

This is Jim and a baby monster.

Jim pushes the pushchair.

Jim gets very tired.

The baby monster pulls Jim home.

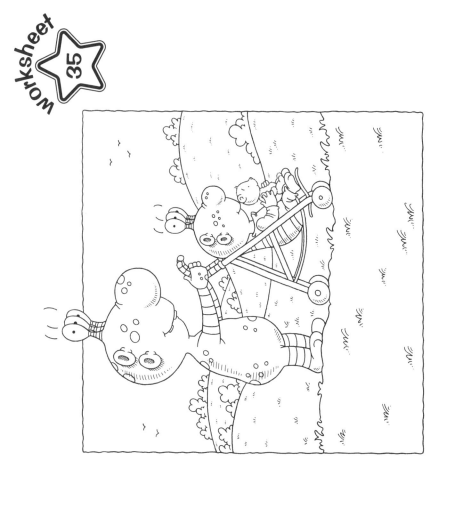

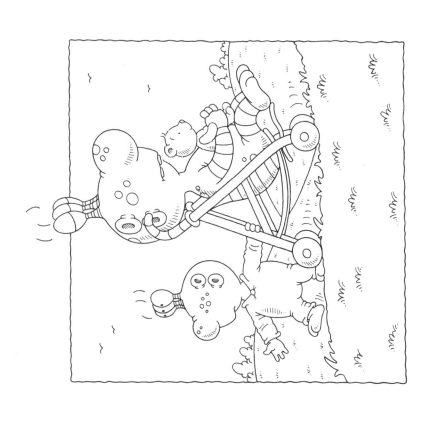

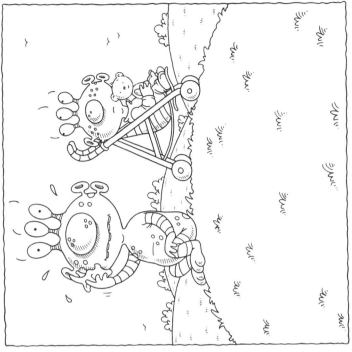

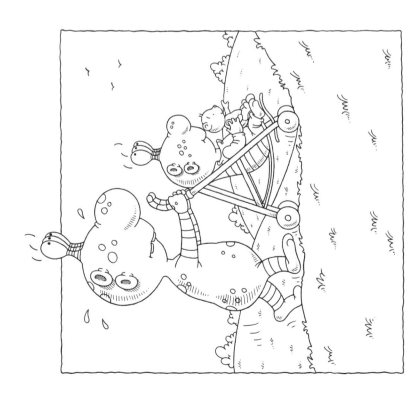

Notes for teachers on Worksheets 37 to 43

The next seven worksheets feature another simple story concerning Jim the monster. The sheets will help the child to begin to create a piece of writing in a narrative form, possibly over several lessons. They also include vocabulary related to the Science topic of 'growing plants'.

Worksheets 37–41

The first four sheets each feature a picture of Jim and a stage in the growth of a plant. These pictures should be photocopied then introduced to the child one at a time and not necessarily in the correct order. In each case ask the child what the picture shows. The opportunity to discuss the picture is an excellent speaking and listening activity. Praise the child for finding all the details in the picture.

Having discussed the pictures, photocopy and cut out the four sentences on Worksheet 41. Read these with the child then help her/him to match the sentences to the pictures to make a story. This sequencing activity provides opportunities for lots of speaking and listening as well as considerable reading practice.

The correct order of the sentences is as follows:

Jim plants a seed in some soil.

Jim gives the seed some water.

The plant begins to grow.

Jim likes the pretty flower.

Worksheets 42–43

Finally, photocopy Worksheets 42 and 43 back to back on to a single sheet. This can then be folded to make a simple four-page book. Support the child in writing a sentence to go with the picture on each page of their book. The child could simply copy the sentences above or you could help her/him to compose her/his own sentences. If this is the case, help her/him to segment the words into their phonemes to be able to spell them.

Andrew Brodie: Supporting Writing Skills © A & C Black Publishers Ltd. 2007

Name:

Date:

Jim plants a seed in some soil.

Jim gives the seed some water.

The plant begins to grow.

Jim likes the pretty flower.

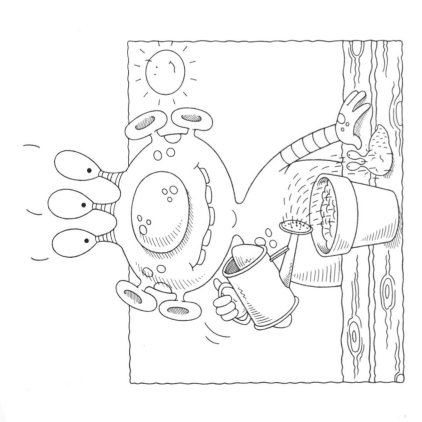

Notes for teachers on Resource sheets A to N

Resource sheets A to M feature a word bank of 156 words. This bank includes all the words that are used on the worksheets in this book together with all the high frequency words recommended for Reception. The sheets should be photocopied and laminated. The words should be cut out individually and, if possible, should each have a piece of velcro attached.

Resource sheet N consists of writing lines on which the featured words can be placed so that the child can create sentences. Photocopy and laminate the sheet and again, if possible, attach the matching velcro strip to enable the words to be placed on this sheet. It is very important that the words can be placed on this sheet so that the writing lines match correctly. When working with the child encourage her/him to place the words carefully with appropriate spaces between them.

In addition to the words you may like to make a simple laminated card showing a full stop.

 Andrew Brodie: Supporting Writing Skills © A & C Black Publishers Ltd. 2007

a	are
address	arm
all	arms
am	asleep
and	at
apple	away

baby	body
banana	book
beach	called
begins	can
big	cat
blue	come

dad	eating
day	eats
dog	eye
ear	eyes
ears	finger
eat	fingers

flower	friend
foot	friends
football	get
for	gives
four	go
Friday	goes

going	has
green	he
grow	He
hair	head
hand	Here
hands	here

holiday	It
home	Jim
I	Jim's
in	leg
is	legs
it	like

likes

monster

list

month

look

much

me

mum

milk

my

Monday

no

nose	paints
of	pear
On	picture
on	plant
orange	plants
painting	play

playing	push
plays	pushchair
pretty	pushes
pull	pushing
pulling	reading
pulls	reads

red	seed
said	she
Saturday	shopping
sea	skateboard
seaside	skipping
see	skips

sleep	swimming
soil	teeth
some	The
story	the
Sunday	they
swim	This

this	toes
three	too
thumb	tooth
Thursday	Tuesday
tired	two
to	up

very	weekend
was	went
water	writes
waving	yellow
we	yes
Wednesday	you

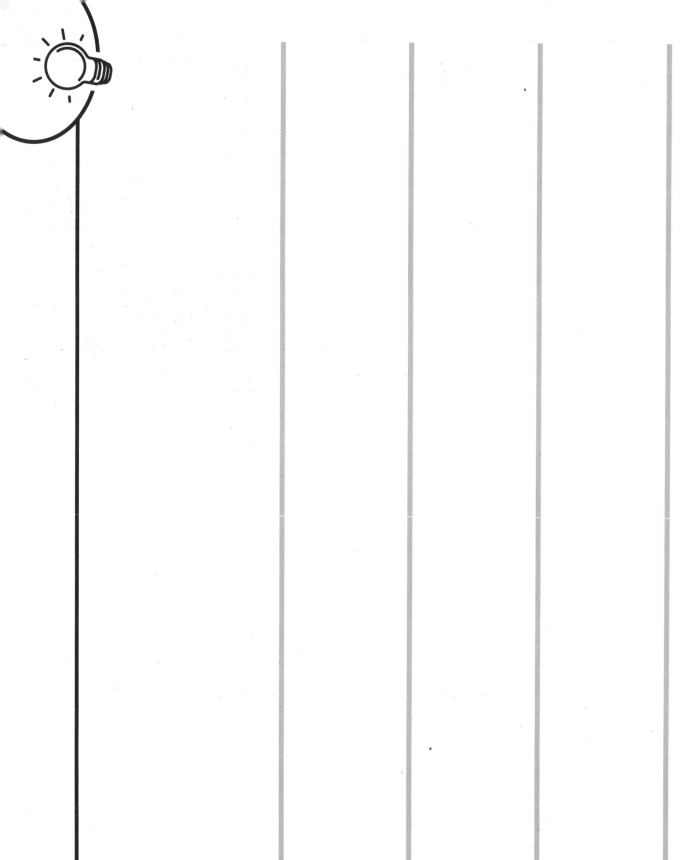